GOD HE REIGNS

GOD HE REIGNS... what a magnificent statement to make! It tells truth – that no matter what you may face in life, God reigns and He is on the Throne!

This album was recorded live in The Sydney Entertainment Centre, where thousands of believers declared that God Reigns in their life. Together we celebrated the goodness of our amazing God!

We pray that as you worship with us, you too will sense the goodness of God, and the timeless truth – that 'God He Reigns'!

Brian & Bobbie Houston,
Senior Pastors, Hillsong Church

IT IS OUR GREATEST PLEASURE and honour to present you with our '05 live album recording... 'God He Reigns'. With all my heart I pray that whatever situation you find yourself in today, whether a season of abundance, or a season of hardship, that you will know that God *does* reign, and may I add, is *completely* in love with you. I pray these songs of faith and adoration will encourage and inspire you to *look up*, to *lift up your head*, and *sing, sing, sing* bringing *all* praise and honour to our awesome Lord and King regardless of your circumstance... that your worship of our Saviour would be rich and authentic... with all your heart, your soul, your mind and your strength. And, lastly, that together, through devoted lives, we would continue to see His Kingdom come on earth, as it is in heaven... and His glory over the earth, like the waters cover the seas... We love you and totally believe in you!

Thank you so very much, Hillsong Worship and Creative Arts teams... Sydney, London, and Kiev. I *love* doing this life with you all and, today, I honour your faithful, fervent, passionate lives for Christ... I am your biggest fan!

Darlene Zschech,
Worship Pastor, Hillsong Church

CONTENTS

COPYRIGHT ENQUIRIES:
Hillsong Publishing
PO Box 1195 Castle Hill
NSW 1765 Australia
Ph: +61 2 8853 5353
Fax: + 61 2 9899 4591
Email: publishing@hillsong.com

Hillsong Publishing is a participant
in the Licence Programs made
available through CCLI throughout
all territories. All reproductions,
including photocopying must occur
under these licences. Please contact
CCLI with enquiries.

'GOD HE REIGNS' is also available
on CD, DVD, Video, Cassette,
Music Book CD, Split Tracks CD
and Split Tracks Cassette.

Let Creation Sing

Words and Music by Reuben Morgan

6

7

high - est___praise._____

Verse 3: Let Your___

Let cre

9

Let Creation Sing

Words and Music by Reuben Morgan

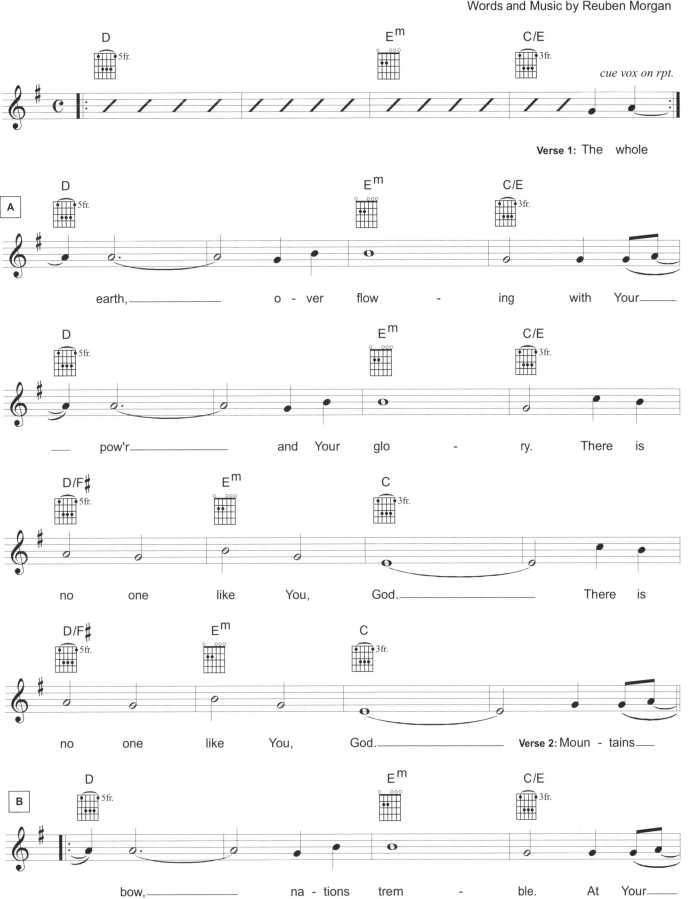

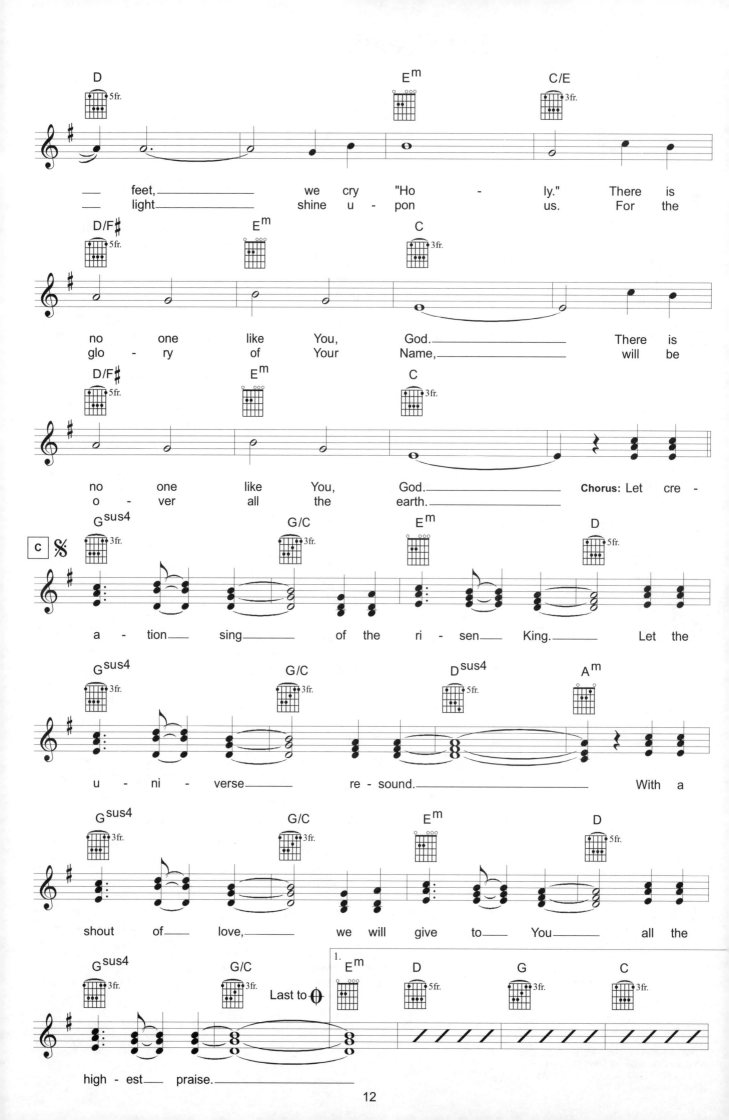

feet,_____ we cry "Ho - ly." There is
light_____ shine u - pon us. For the

no one like You, God._____ There is
glo - ry of Your Name,_____ will be

no one like You, God._____ **Chorus:** Let cre -
o - ver all the earth._____

a - tion___ sing___ of the ri - sen__ King.___ Let the

u - ni - verse___ re - sound._____ With a

shout of__ love,___ we will give to__ You__ all the

high - est__ praise._____

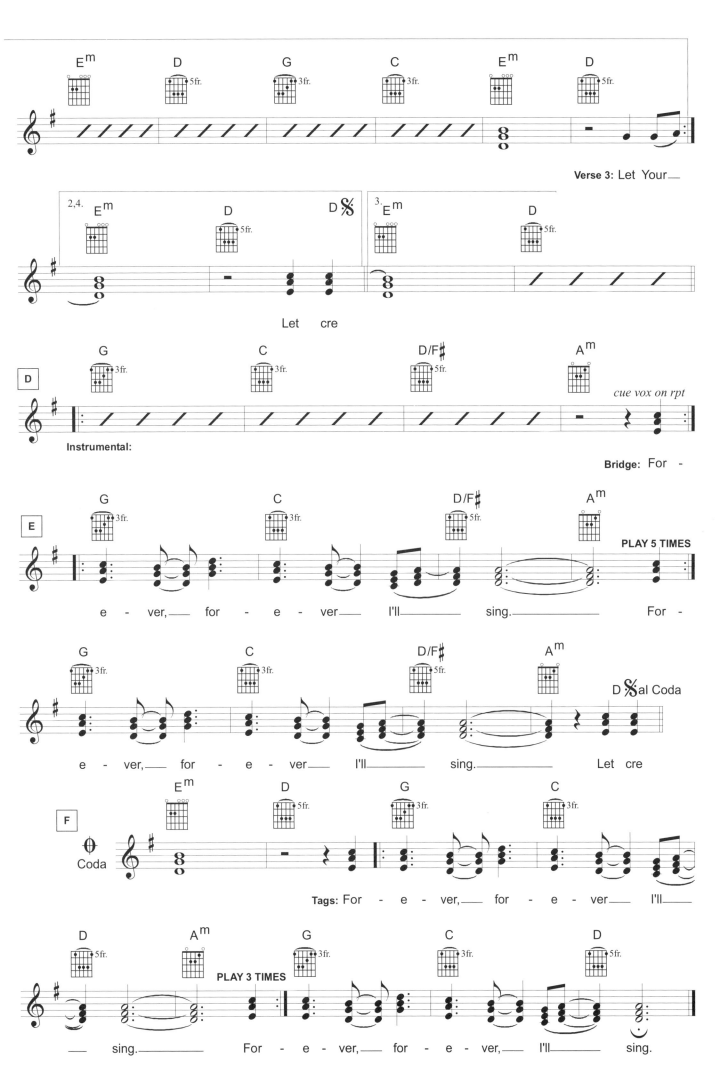

13

LET CREATION SING

Words and Music by Reuben Morgan

VERSE 1:
The whole earth
Overflowing
With Your power
And Your glory
There is no one like You God
There is no one like You God

VERSE 2:
Mountains bow
Nations tremble
At Your feet we cry holy
There is no one like You God
There is no one like You God

CHORUS:
Let creation sing of the risen King
Let the universe resound
With a shout of love
We will give to You
All the highest praise

VERSE 3:
**Let Your light
Shine upon us
Let Your light
Shine upon us
For the glory of Your Name
Will be over all the earth**

BRIDGE:
**Forever
Forever I'll sing
Forever
Forever I'll sing**

Salvation Is Here

And I don't care what the world throws at me now,
All in all that the world would know Your Name.

It's gon-na be al-right.

It's gon-na

be al - right. **Chorus:** 'Cause I know my___ God___ saved the day.___ And I know___

___ His___ Word___ ne - ver fails.___ And I know___ my___ God___

Last to ⊕   made a way___ for me._____   Sal - va - tion is

D.C.

Salvation Is Here

Words and Music by Joel Houston

No rpt on DC

Verse 1: God a - bove all the world in mo - tion.
Verse 2: Hear the sound of the gen - e - ra - tions,

God a - bove all my hopes and fears.
ma - king loud our free - dom song.

And I don't care what the world throws at me now,
All in all that the world would know Your Name.

It's gon-na be al - right.

It's gon - na

be al - right. **Chorus:** 'Cause I know my___ God___ saved the day.___ And I know___

___ His___ Word___ ne - ver fails.___ And I know___ my___ God___

___ made a way___ for me._____ Sal - va - tion is

It's gon-na be al - right.___ 'Cause I

Sal - va - tion is___ here._____

_____ **Bridge:** Sal - va - tion___ is___ here.___

Sal - va - tion___ is here, and He lives in me.___ Sal - va - tion___ is___

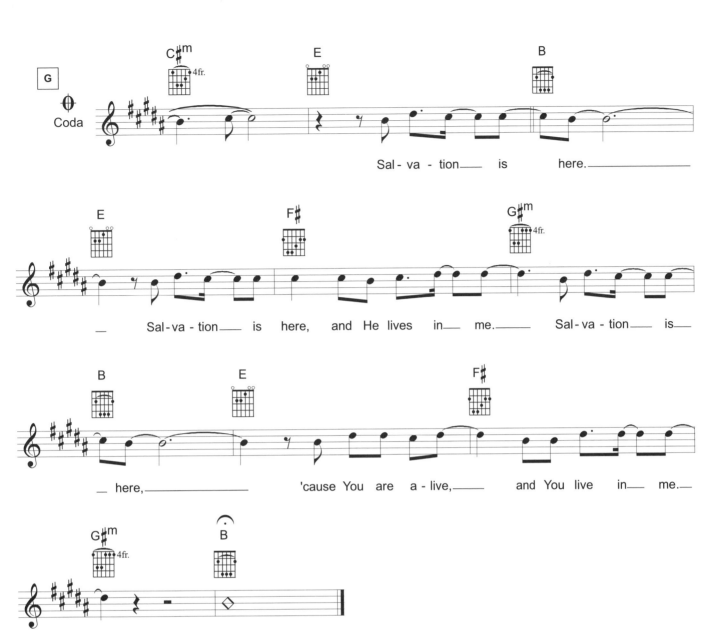

Sal - va - tion___ is   here.___

___ Sal - va - tion___ is   here,   and He lives in___ me.___ Sal - va - tion___ is___

___ here,_____ 'cause You are a - live,_____   and You live in___ me.___

___

27

SALVATION IS HERE

Words and Music by Joel Houston

VERSE 1:
God above all the world in motion
God above all my hopes and fears
And I don't care
What the world throws at me now
It's gonna be alright

VERSE 2:
Hear the sound of the generations
Making loud our freedom song
All in all that the world
Would know Your Name
It's gonna be alright

CHORUS:
'Cause I know my God saved the day
And I know His Word never fails
And I know my God made a way for me
Salvation is here

Hillsong
MUSIC AUSTRALIA

© 2004 Joel Houston / Hillsong Publishing
PO Box 1195 Castle Hill NSW 1765 Australia
PH 61 2 8853 5353   FAX 61 2 9899 4591
E-Mail: publishing@hillsong.com

BRIDGE:
Salvation is here
Salvation is here and He lives in me
Salvation is here
Salvation that died just to set me free

Salvation is here
Salvation is here and He lives in me
Salvation is here
'Cause You are alive and You live in me

His Love

Words and Music by Raymond Badham

Verse: Your light is o - ver __ me, __ floo-ding o - ver __ me __

33

Bridge: You brought the sun - shine in, and turned the dark to day.

You made the sha - dows flee a - way

You o - pened up my eyes to a new and li - ving way.

The daw - ning of a brand new

His Love

Words and Music by Raymond Badham

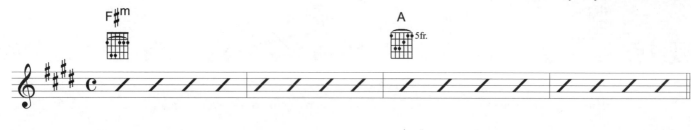

Verse: Your light is o - ver___ me,___ floo-ding o - ver___ me

the night is lif - ted.

Hea-ven o - ver___ me floo-ding o - ver___ me.

I can't con - tain it.___

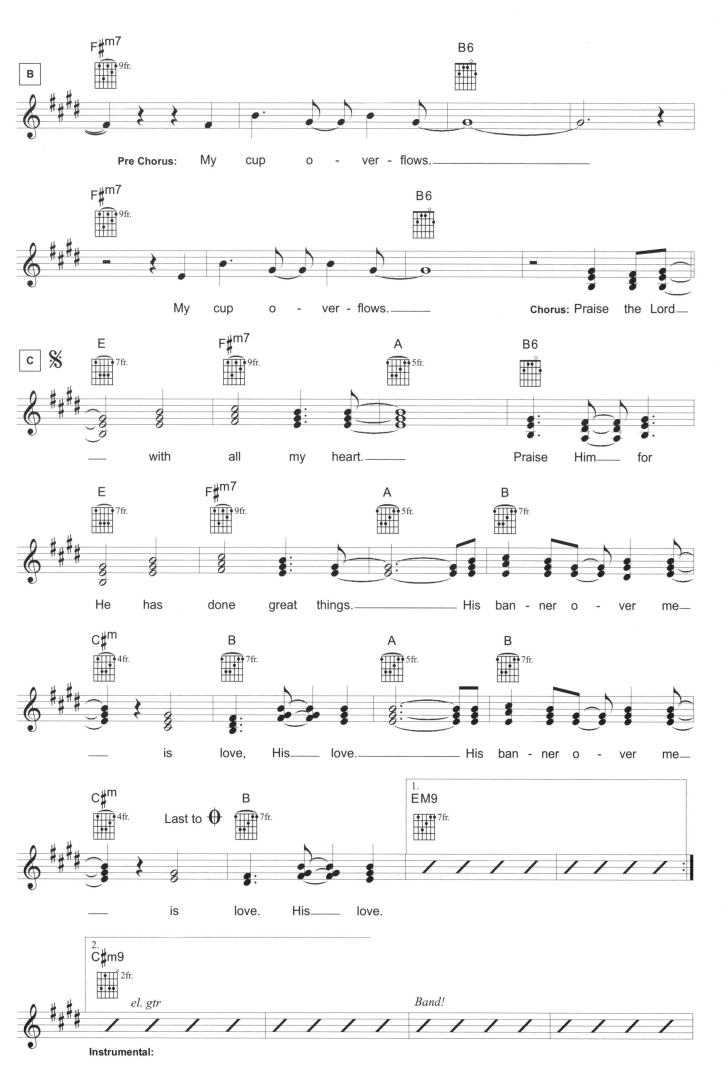

B

F#m7   B6

Pre Chorus: My cup o - ver - flows._____

F#m7   B6

My cup o - ver - flows._____   **Chorus:** Praise the Lord___

C 𝄋

E   F#m7   A   B6

___ with all my heart._____   Praise Him___ for

E   F#m7   A   B

He has done great things._____ His ban - ner o - ver me___

C#m   B   A   B

___ is love, His___ love._____ His ban - ner o - ver me___

C#m   Last to ⊕   B

1.
EM9

___ is love. His___ love.

2.
C#m9

el. gtr   *Band!*

Instrumental:

39

Bridge: You brought the sun - shine in, and turned the dark to day.

You made the sha - dows flee a - way

You o - pened up my eyes to a new and li - ving way.

The daw - ning of a brand new

day. Praise the Lord

His love Chorus 2: Praise the Lord with

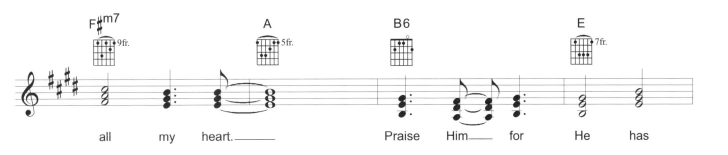

all   my   heart._____   Praise   Him___   for   He   has

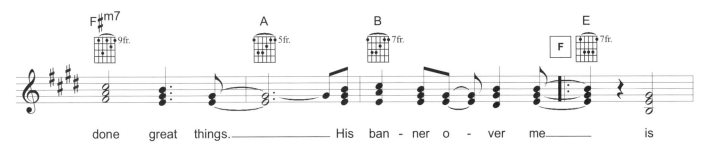

done   great   things._____   His ban - ner o - ver me_____   is

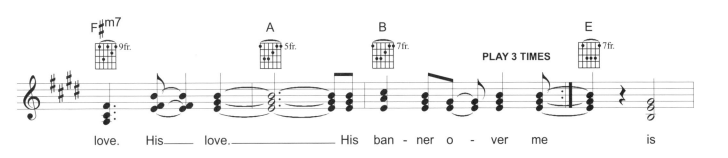

love.   His___   love._____   His ban - ner o - ver me   is

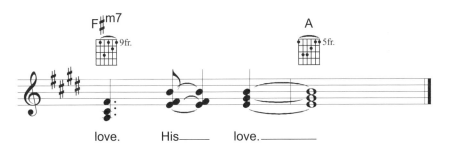

love.   His___   love._____

HIS LOVE

Words and Music by Raymond Badham

VERSE:
Your light is over me
Flooding over me
The night is lifted
Heaven over me
Flooding over me
I can't contain it

PRE CHORUS:
My cup overflows
My cup overflows

CHORUS:
Praise the Lord
With all my heart
Praise Him for
He has done great things
His banner over me is love
His love
His banner over me is love
His love

Hillsong
MUSIC AUSTRALIA

BRIDGE:
**You brought the sunshine in
And turned the dark to day
You made the shadows flee away
You opened up my eyes
To a new and living way
The dawning of a brand new day**

Emmanuel

Words and Music by Reuben Morgan

us.   You make all things___ new.   **Chorus:** Em-man-u-el,
name.   I will fol - low___ You.

Je-sus___ Christ,   You'll ne-ver let me go.___

My Shep-herd___ King,   You're wat-ching o - ver me,   Em-man-u-

Emmanuel

Words and Music by Reuben Morgan

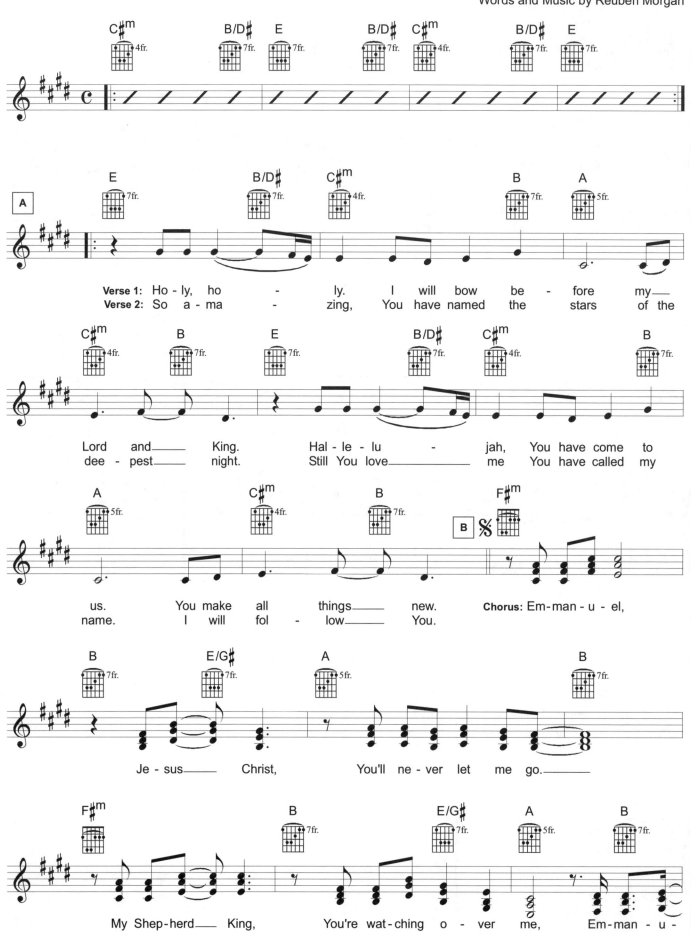

51

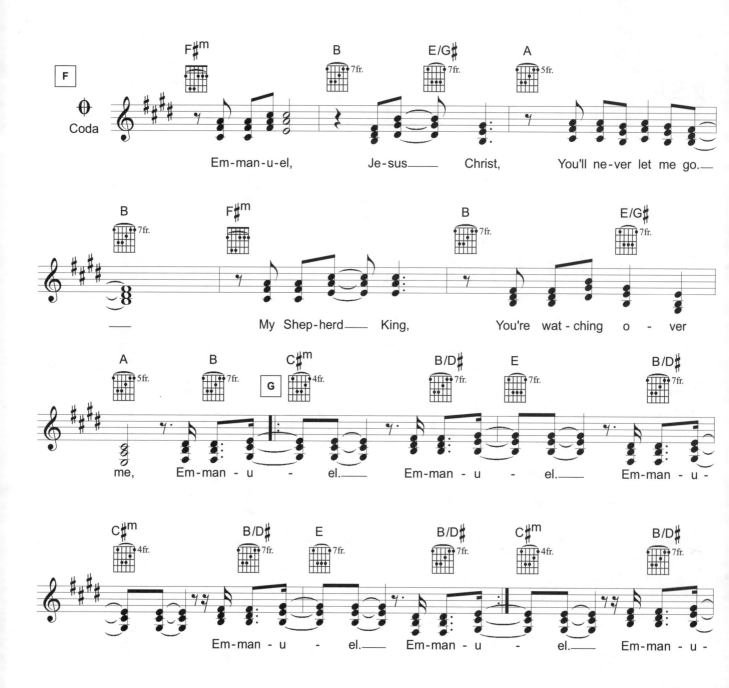

Em-man-u-el, Je-sus Christ, You'll ne-ver let me go.

My Shep-herd King, You're wat-ching o - ver

me, Em-man - u - el. Em-man - u - el. Em-man - u -

Em-man - u - el. Em-man - u - el. Em-man - u -

el.

EMMANUEL

Words and Music by Reuben Morgan

VERSE 1:
Holy holy
I will bow before
My Lord and King
Hallelujah
You have come to us
You make all things new

CHORUS:
Emmanuel
Jesus Christ
You'll never let me go
My Shepherd King
You're watching over me
Emmanuel

VERSE 2:
So amazing
You have named the stars
Of the deepest night
Still You love me
You have called my name
I will follow You

Hillsong
MUSIC AUSTRALIA

© 2005 Reuben Morgan / Hillsong Publishing
PO Box 1195 Castle Hill NSW 1765 Australia
PH 61 2 8853 5353   FAX 61 2 9899 4591
E-Mail: publishing@hillsong.com

BRIDGE:
Holy holy
God Almighty
There is none like You
Holy holy
God Almighty
There is none like You

Saviour

Words and Music by Darlene Zschech

Verse 1: A Sa - viour on a hill, dy - ing for my shame. Could this be true? De - fies the world I see.

Yet this is all my heart_____ was long - ing_____ for._____ To

know You,_____ my Lord._____ To know_____ You, Lord._____ To

Chorus 1: You de - serve,_____ You de - serve._____ You de - serve_____ all the praise._____

PLAY 3 TIMES

Hal - le - lu - jah, we will sing for - e - ver.

Hal - le - lu - jah to the King. Hal - le - lu - jah, we will sing

D % al Coda

for - e - ver.

60

Saviour

You de - serve,_____ You de - serve._____

You de - serve_____ all the praise._____

C 𝄋

Verse 2: The hea - vens wept for You._____ The earth cried out_____ 'Could_____
Verse 3: And all hu - ma - ni - ty_____ aches to find this beau -

_____ He be_____ the One?'_____ For You so loved the_____world,_____
ti - ful love_____ You give._____ We come to You a - gain_____

You gave Your on - ly_____ Son_____ to say_____ I love you_____
to of - fer up our lives_____ to wor - ship_____ You_____ a -

so._____ Oh how_____ I love_____ You_____ so._____
lone._____ To wor - ship You_____ a - lone._____

D

Chorus 2: You de - serve,_____ You de - serve._____ You de - serve_____ all the praise._____

63

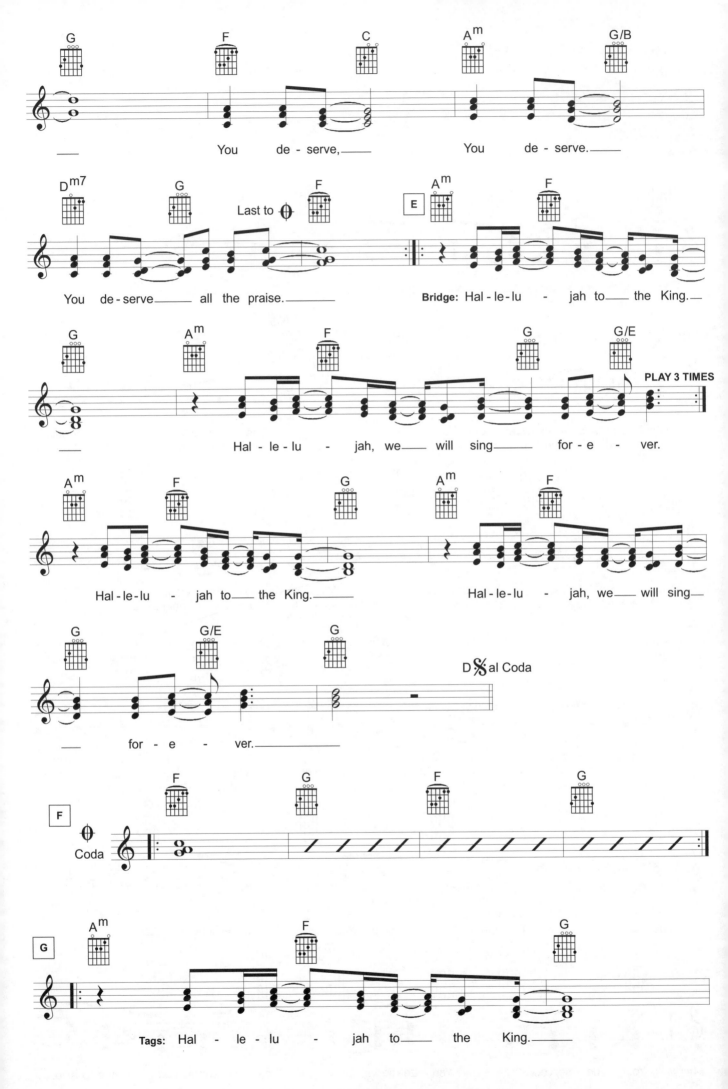

You de - serve,____ You de - serve.____

You de - serve____ all the praise.____ **Bridge:** Hal - le - lu - jah to____ the King.____

Hal - le - lu - jah, we____ will sing____ for - e - ver. PLAY 3 TIMES

Hal - le - lu - jah to____ the King.____ Hal - le - lu - jah, we____ will sing____

____ for - e - ver.____ D.S. al Coda

Coda

Last to ⊕

Tags: Hal - le - lu - jah to____ the King.____

64

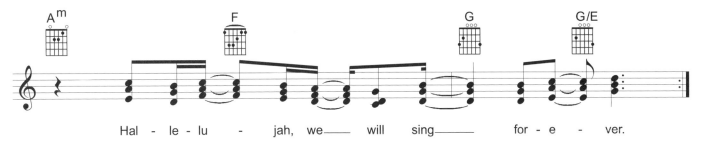

Hal - le - lu - jah, we____ will   sing____   for - e - ver.

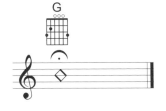

SAVIOUR

Words and Music by Darlene Zschech

VERSE 1:
**A Saviour on a hill dying for my shame
Could this be true?
Defies the world I see
Yet this is all my heart was longing for
To know You my Lord
To know You Lord**

CHORUS:
**You deserve
You deserve
You deserve all the praise**

VERSE 2:
**The heavens wept for You
The earth cried out 'Could He be the One?'
For You so loved the world
You gave Your only Son to say
I love you so
Oh how I love You so**

Hillsong
MUSIC AUSTRALIA

BRIDGE:
**Hallelujah to the King
Hallelujah we will sing forever**

VERSE 3:
**And all humanity
Aches to find this beautiful love You give
We come to You again
To offer up our lives
To worship You alone
To worship You alone**

Wonderful God

♩= 71

Words and Music by Ned Davies

wor-thy of ___ our wor - ship, ___ and wor-thy of ___ our love. ___ We stand in awe of

all You are.

Verse: Beau-ti-ful ___ is Your cre-a - tion. ___ You're glo-ri - ous in ev-ery way. ___

Wonderful God

♩ = 71

Words and Music by Ned Davies

Won-der - ful God._____ Won-der - ful, O God._____ Won-der

ful O God._____ **Chorus 1:** You are wor - thy of___ all glo - ry,___ all

ho-nour, and___ all praise.___ All to You___ our God,___ for - e - ver and___ al-ways.___ You are

wor - thy of___ our wor - ship,___ and wor - thy of___ our love.___ We stand in awe of

all You are.

Verse: Beau - ti - ful___ is Your cre - a - tion.___ You're glo - ri - ous in ev - ery way.___

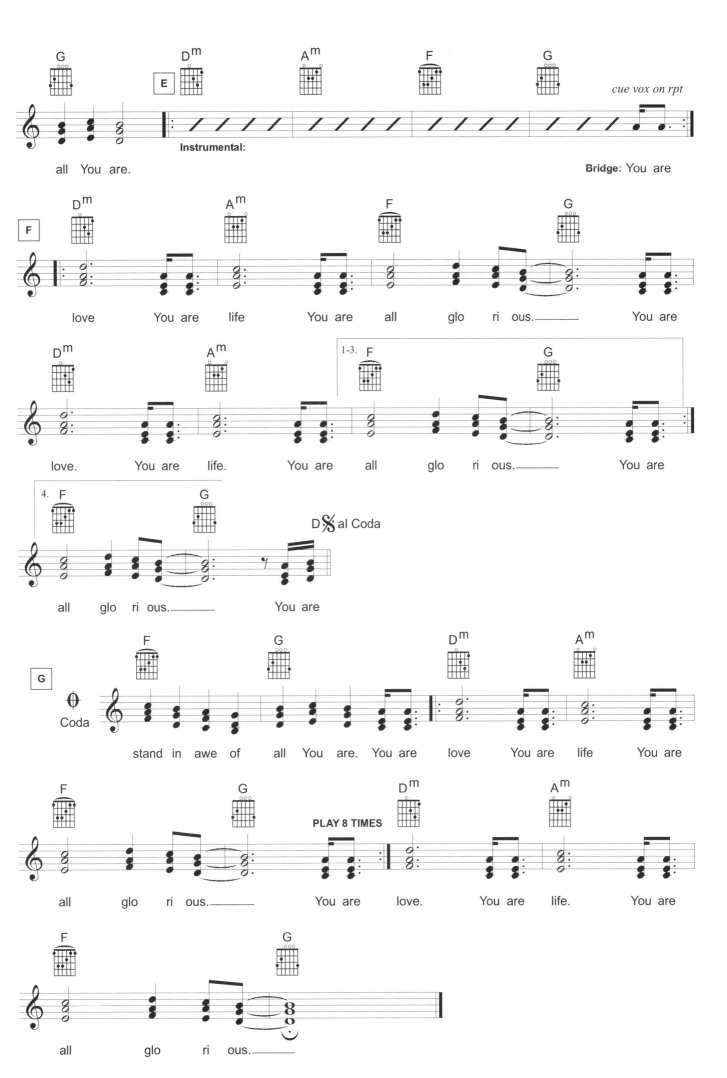

77

WONDERFUL GOD

Words and Music by Ned Davies

VERSE:
Beautiful is Your creation
You're glorious in every way
You surround us with
Your faithful love
And we can trust in all You say

PRE CHORUS:
Wonderful God
Wonderful O God

CHORUS:
You are worthy of all glory
All honour and all praise
All to You our God
Forever and always
You are worthy of our worship
And worthy of our love
We stand in awe of
All You are

© 2005 Ned Davies / Hillsong Publishing
PO Box 1195 Castle Hill NSW 1765 Australia
PH 61 2 8853 5353   FAX 61 2 9899 4591
E-Mail: publishing@hillsong.com

BRIDGE:
You are love
You are life
You are all glorious
You are love
You are life
You are all glorious

God He Reigns with All I Need Is You

Words and Music by Marty Sampson

God He Reigns with All I Need Is You

Words and Music by Marty Sampson

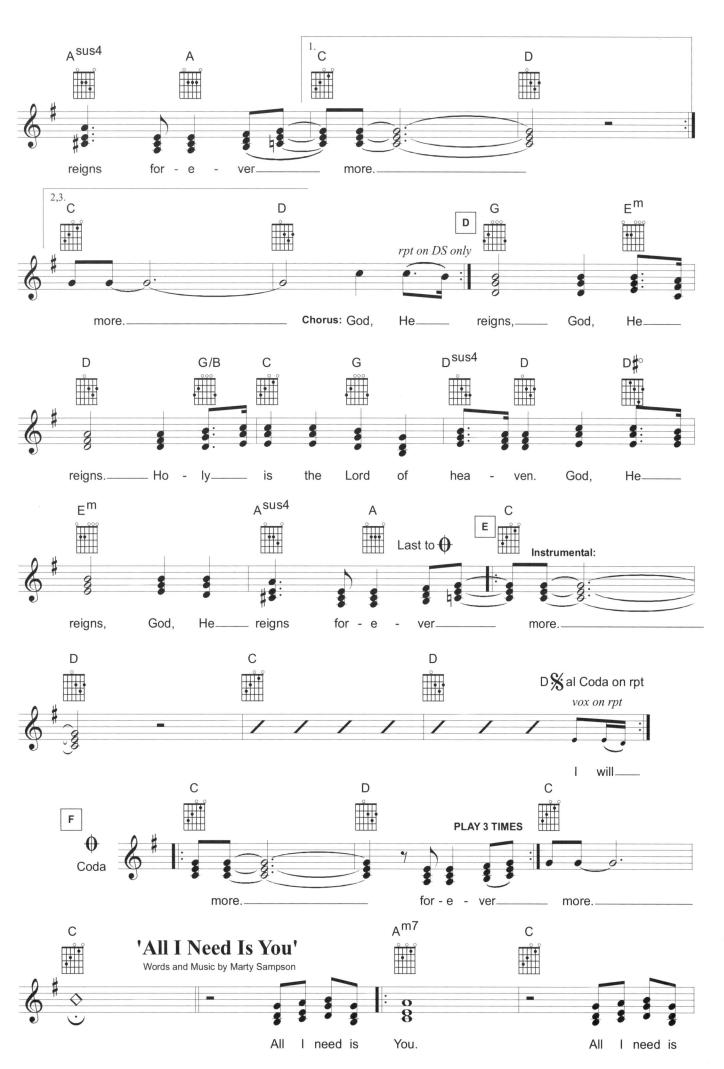

'All I Need Is You'

Words and Music by Marty Sampson

You, Lord.   Is You,   Lord.   All I need is   You.   All I need is

You,   Lord.   Is You,   Lord.   **Chorus:** God, He——

reigns,—— God, He—— reigns.—— Ho - ly—— is the Lord of

hea - ven. God, He—— reigns, God, He—— reigns for - e - ver——

Fine   **Rpt al FINE**

more.——

GOD HE REIGNS with ALL I NEED IS YOU

Words and Music by Marty Sampson

VERSE:
Holy One
Holy One
All creation bows to worship
Hallelujah
Hallelujah
Glory in the highest

PRE CHORUS:
I will sing
I will sing His praises forever

CHORUS:
God He reigns
God He reigns
Holy is the Lord of heaven
God He reigns
God He reigns forever more

INTERLUDE:
All I need is You
All I need is You Lord
Is You Lord

Hillsong
MUSIC AUSTRALIA

© 2004 Marty Sampson / Hillsong Publishing
PO Box 1195 Castle Hill NSW 1765 Australia
PH 61 2 8853 5353   FAX 61 2 9899 4591
E-Mail: publishing@hillsong.com

Yours Is The Kingdom

Words and Music by Joel Houston

God for-e-ver all the glo - ry, Lord_____ is_____ Yours._____

PLAY 3 TIMES

Yours Is The Kingdom

Words and Music by Joel Houston

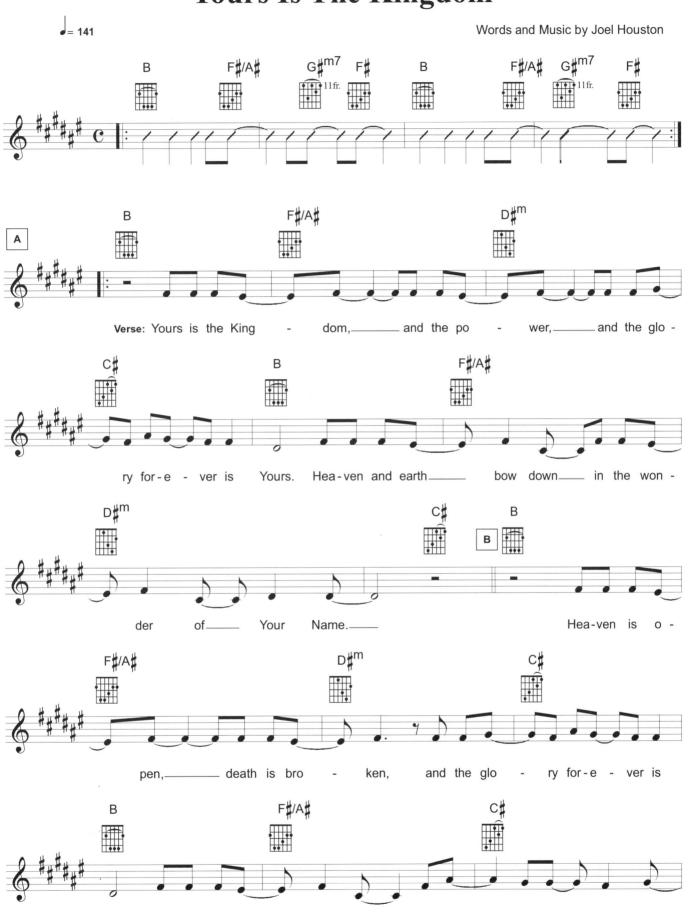

Pre Chorus: King a-bove kings, all the u-ni-verse will sing, e-ver-las-ting God, You are won-der-ful. You are won-der-ful. Chorus: And the shout of the earth will be Your praise, God for-e-ver. And the light un-to all will be Your won-der-ful Name. For the glo-ry Lord is Yours. God, for-e-ver, all the

100

YOURS IS THE KINGDOM

Words and Music by Joel Houston

VERSE:
Yours is the Kingdom
And the power
And the glory forever is Yours
Heaven and earth bow down
In the wonder of Your Name
Heaven is open
Death is broken
And the glory forever is Yours
Nothing can overcome
The power of Your Name

PRE CHORUS:
King above kings
All the universe will sing
Everlasting God
You are wonderful
You are wonderful

© 2005 Joel Houston / Hillsong Publishing
PO Box 1195 Castle Hill NSW 1765 Australia
PH 61 2 8853 5353   FAX 61 2 9899 4591
E-Mail: publishing@hillsong.com

CHORUS:
**And the shout of the earth
Will be Your praise
God forever
And the light unto all
Will be Your wonderful Name
For the glory Lord is Yours
God forever
All the glory Lord is Yours**

Welcome In This Place

Words and Music by Miriam Webster

Verse 1: Ho - ly Spi - rit. Ho - ly Spi - rit. sent from hea - ven. The
Verse 2: Ho - ly Spi - rit, Spi - rit, sent from hea - ven. The
Verse 3: Clo - sest friend, here in Your pre - sence is

Com - for - ter, Coun - sel - lor here.
God of all glo - ry is here.
full - ness of joy o - ver - flo

cue notes 3rd vse

107

rate my soul.   **Instrumental:**

Cue Vox **PLAY 4 TIMES**

Pre Chorus 2: Rise up wi-thin me, Li - ving Wa - ter,

Spi - rit of God in me.   **Chorus:** You are

D.S. al Coda

108

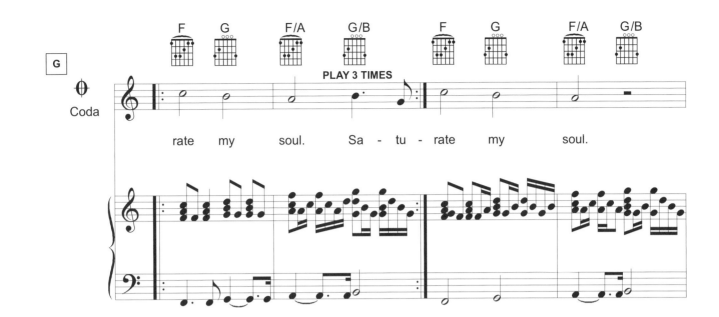

G **Coda**

PLAY 3 TIMES

rate my soul. Sa - tu - rate my soul.

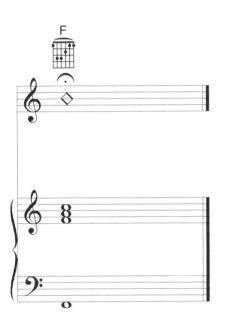

Welcome In This Place

♩ = 75

Words and Music by Miriam Webster

Verse 1: Ho - ly___ Spi - rit.___ Ho - ly___ Spi - rit.___
Verse 2: Ho - ly___ Spi - rit,___ sent from___ hea - ven.___ The
Verse 3: Clo - sest___ friend, here___ in Your___ pre - sence___ is

cue notes 3rd vse

Com - for - ter, Coun - sel - lor here._____
God of___ all glo - ry___ is here.
full - ness___ of joy o - ver - flo

wing._____ **Pre Chorus:** Rise up wi - thin___ me, Li - ving Wa - ter,

Spi - rit___ of God___ in___ me.___ **Chorus:** You are wel - come in___ this place.

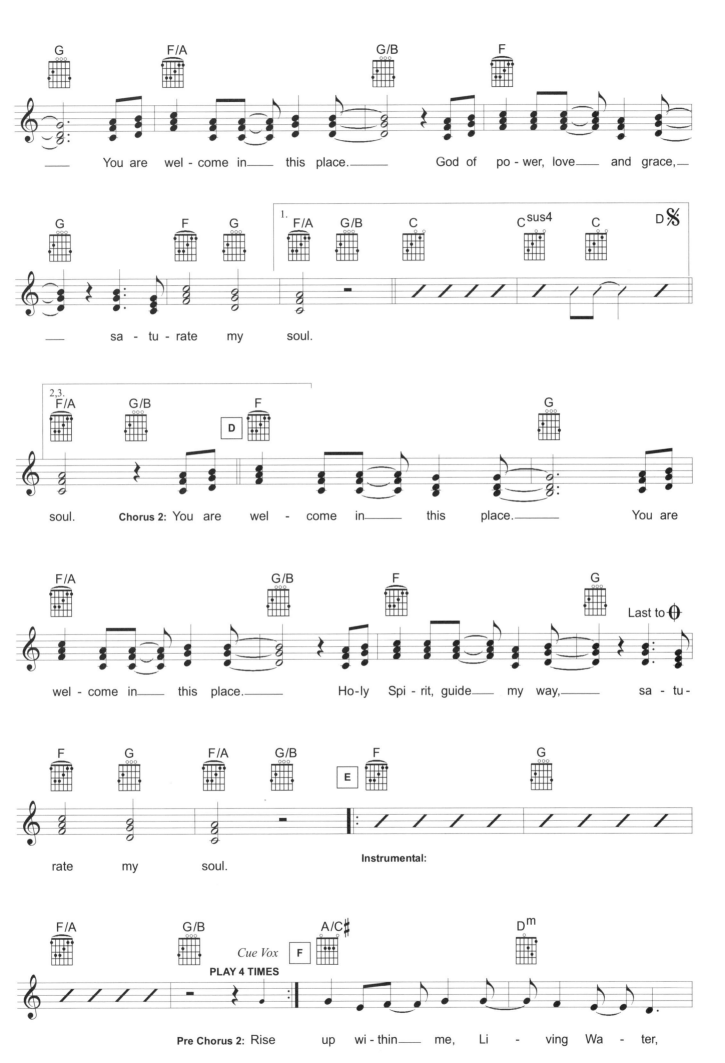

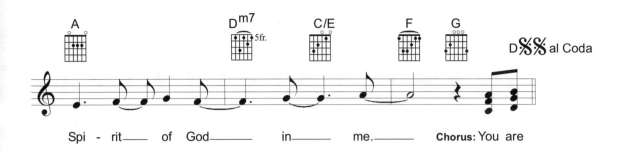

Spi - rit___ of God___ in___ me.___ **Chorus:** You are

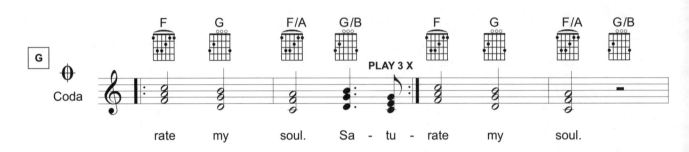

rate   my   soul.   Sa - tu - rate   my   soul.

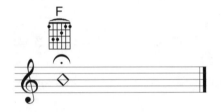

WELCOME IN THIS PLACE

Words and Music by Miriam Webster

VERSE 1:
Holy Spirit
Holy Spirit
Comforter Counsellor here

VERSE 2:
Holy Spirit sent from heaven
The God of all glory is here

PRE CHORUS:
Rise up within me
Living Water
Spirit of God in me

CHORUS:
You are welcome in this place
You are welcome in this place
God of power love and grace
Saturate my soul

CHORUS 2:
You are welcome in this place
You are welcome in this place
Holy Spirit guide my way
Saturate my soul

Hillsong
MUSIC AUSTRALIA

© 2005 Miriam Webster / Hillsong Publishing
PO Box 1195 Castle Hill NSW 1765 Australia
PH 61 2 8853 5353   FAX 61 2 9899 4591
E-Mail: publishing@hillsong.com

VERSE 3:
**Closest friend
Here in Your presence
Is fullness of joy overflowing**

Let Us Adore

Words and Music by Reuben Morgan

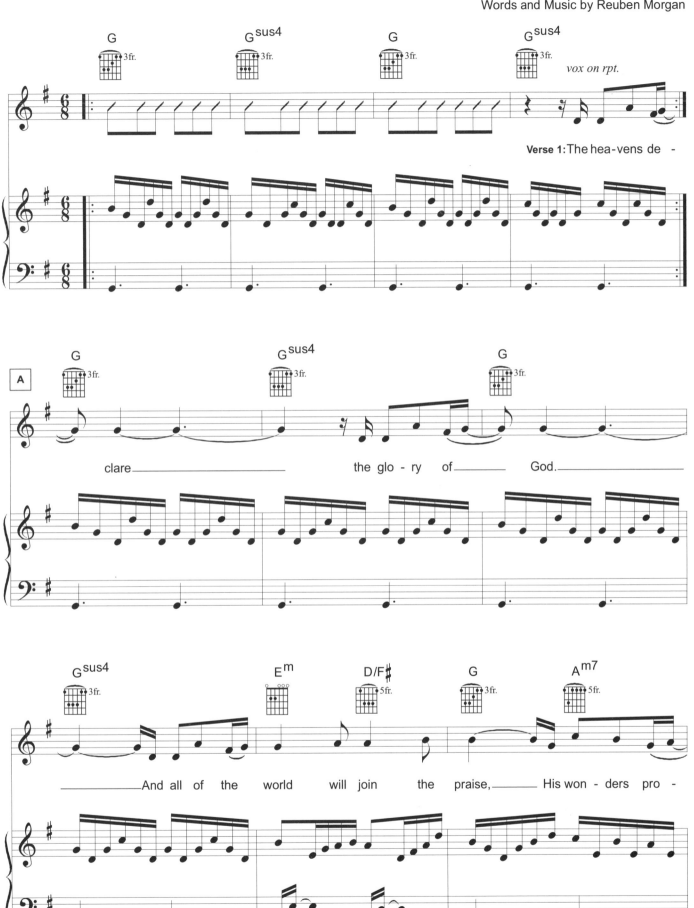

Chorus: Let us a-dore Him, let us a-dore Him. Je-sus Christ is the Lord. Verse 3: E-ter-ni-ty's

118

Instrumental:

Bridge: Hal - le -

Je - sus Christ is the Lord.

Je - sus Christ is the Lord.

Let Us Adore

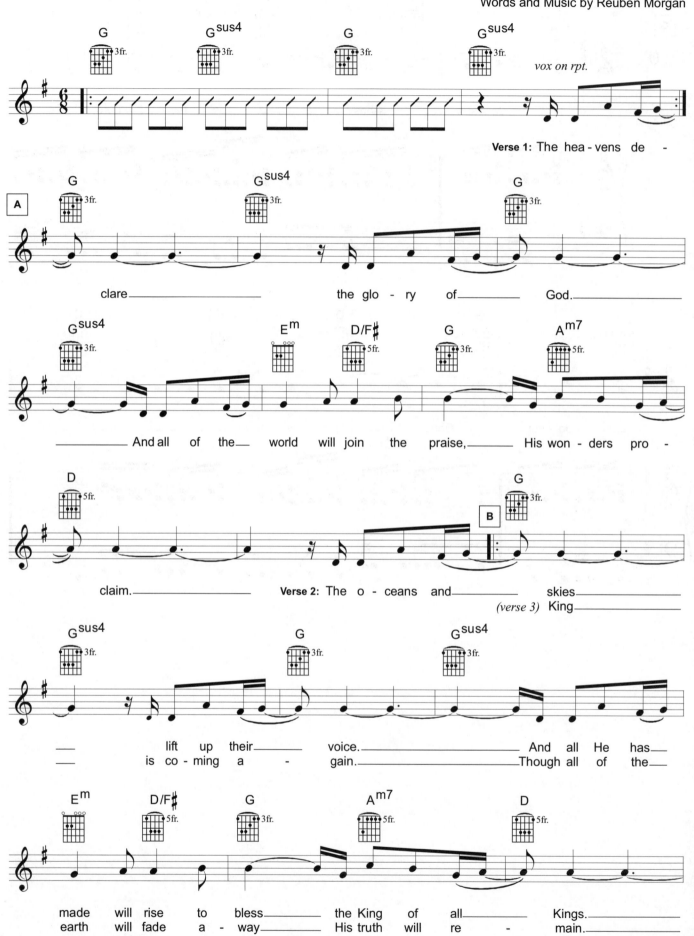

© 2005 Reuben Morgan / Hillsong Publishing
PO Box 1195 Castle Hill NSW 1765 Australia
Ph: 61 2 8853 5353 Fax: 61 2 9899 4591
Email: publishing@hillsong.com

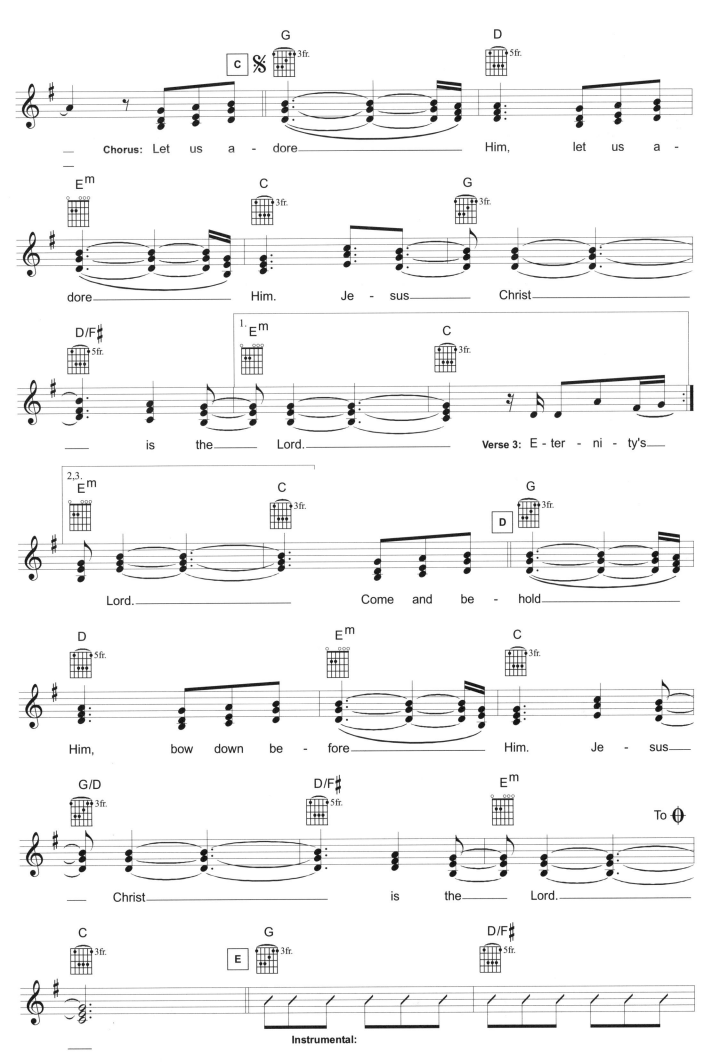

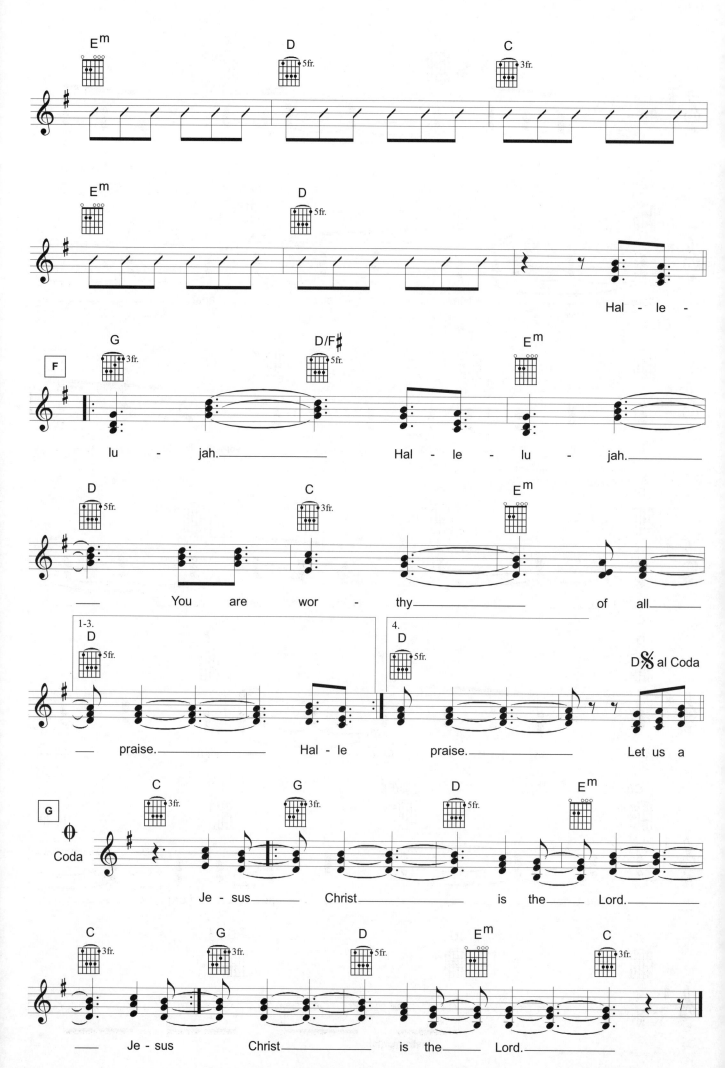

LET US ADORE

Words and Music by Reuben Morgan

VERSE 1:
**The heavens declare
The glory of God
And all of the world
Will join the praise
His wonders proclaim**

VERSE 2:
**The oceans and skies
Lift up their voice
And all He has made
Will rise to bless
The King of all kings**

CHORUS:
**Let us adore Him
Let us adore Him
Jesus Christ is the Lord**

CHORUS 2:
**Come and behold Him
Bow down before Him
Jesus Christ is the Lord**

Hillsong
MUSIC AUSTRALIA

© 2005 Reuben Morgan / Hillsong Publishing
PO Box 1195 Castle Hill NSW 1765 Australia
PH 61 2 8853 5353   FAX 61 2 9899 4591
E-Mail: publishing@hillsong.com

VERSE 3:
Eternity's King
Is coming again
Though all of the earth
Will fade away
His truth will remain

BRIDGE:
Hallelujah
Hallelujah
You are worthy of all praise

All For Love

$\quad\bullet = 67$

Words and Music by Mia Fieldes

Vox Adlib on rpt.

Verse 1: All for love,___ a Fa - ther gave.___

I will join___ the an - gel song.___

E - ver ho - ly is___ the Lord,___

King of glo - ry, King___ of all.___ Oh how ma - ny times

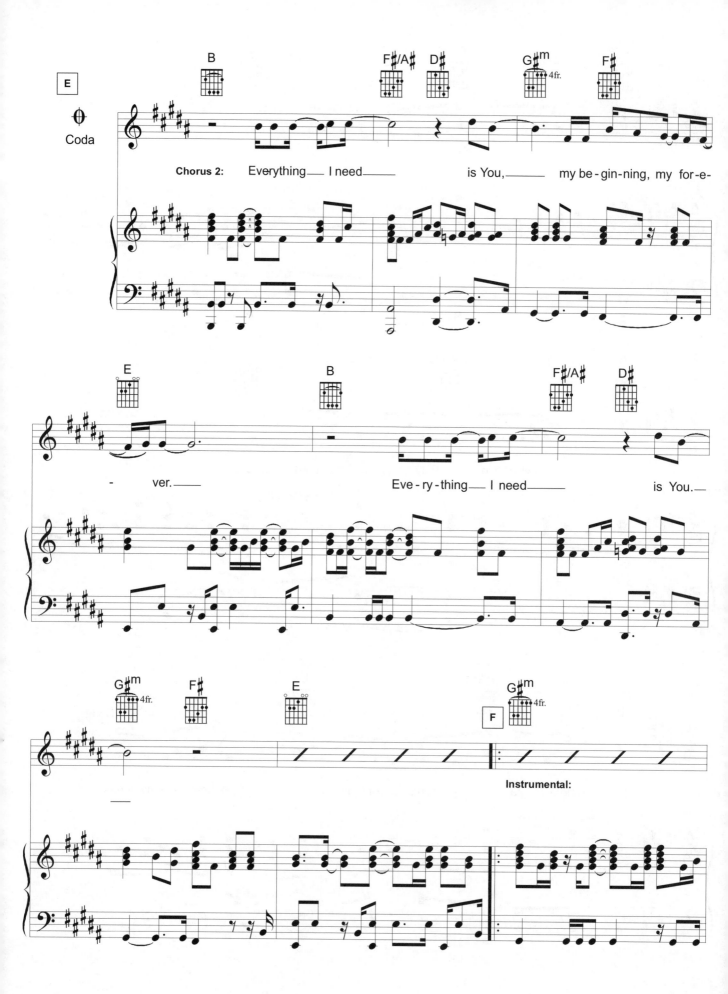

Verse 3: All for love___ a Sa - viour prayed,___

Ab - ba Fa - ther, have___ Your way.___

133

Though they know＿ not what＿ they do.＿

Let the cross＿ draw man＿ to You. ＿ To You.＿＿ To You.

＿＿ To You.＿ **Chorus 3:** Eve-ry-thing＿ I need＿

All For Love

♩ = 67

Words and Music by Mia Fieldes

Vox Adlib on rpt.

All

for love for love was cru - ci - fied.

A

Verse 1: All for love, a Fa - ther gave.

For on - ly love could make a way.

All for love, the hea - ven's cried,

for love was cru - ci - fied. **Pre Chorus:** Oh how ma - ny times

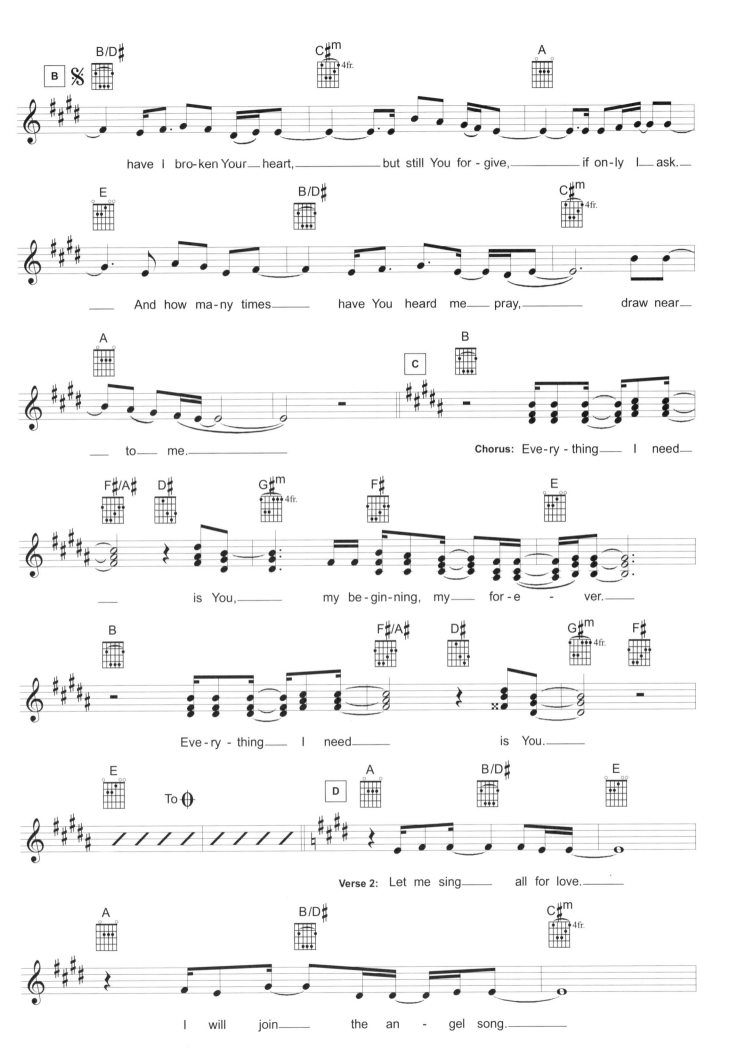

have I bro-ken Your heart, but still You for - give, if on-ly I ask.

And how ma-ny times have You heard me pray, draw near

to me. **Chorus:** Eve-ry - thing I need

is You, my be-gin-ning, my for - e - ver.

Eve-ry - thing I need is You.

Verse 2: Let me sing all for love.

I will join the an - gel song.

137

ALL FOR LOVE

Words and Music by Mia Fieldes

VERSE 1:
All for love a Father gave
For only love could make a way
All for love the heavens cried
For love was crucified

PRE CHORUS:
Oh how many times
Have I broken Your heart
But still You forgive
If only I ask
And how many times
Have You heard me pray
Draw near to me

CHORUS:
Everything I need is You
My beginning my forever
Everything I need is You

Hillsong
MUSIC AUSTRALIA

© 2004 Mia Fieldes / Hillsong Publishing
PO Box 1195 Castle Hill NSW 1765 Australia
PH 61 2 8853 5353   FAX 61 2 9899 4591
E-Mail: publishing@hillsong.com

VERSE 2:
Let me sing all for love
I will join the angel song
Ever holy is the Lord
King of glory King of all

VERSE 3:
All for love a Saviour prayed
Abba Father have Your way
Though they know not what they do
Let the cross draw man to You

Know You More

Words and Music by Darlene Zschech

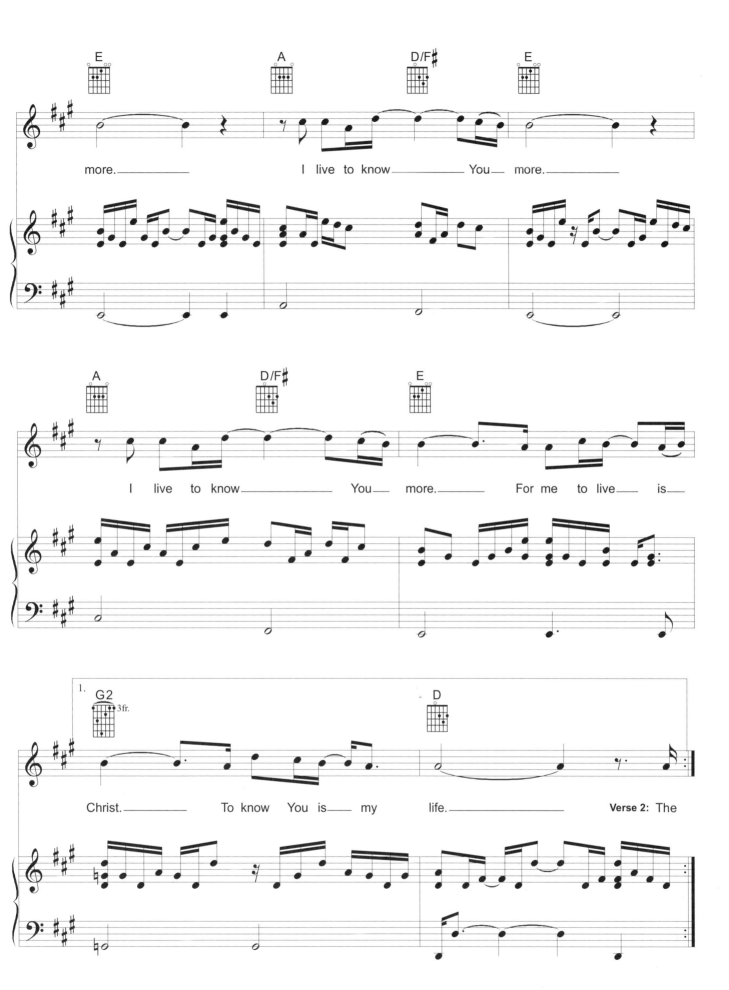

more._____ I live to know_____ You__ more._____

I live to know_____ You__ more._____ For me to live__ is__

1.

Christ._____ To know You is__ my life._____ **Verse 2:** The

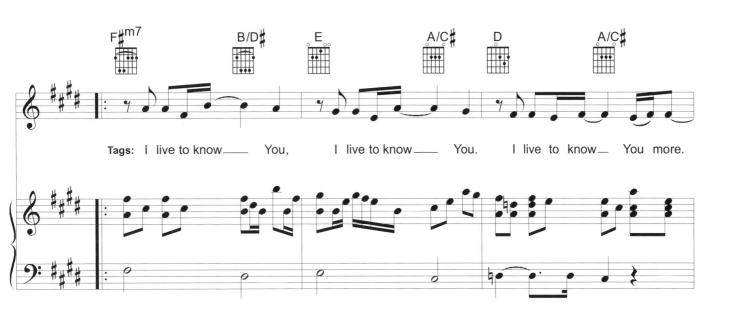

Tags: I live to know ____ You, I live to know ____ You. I live to know ____ You more.

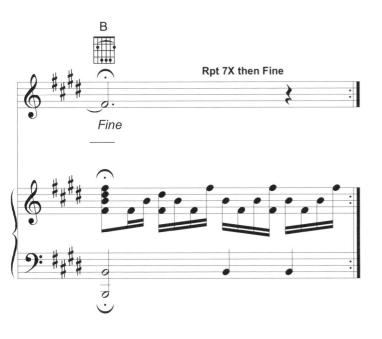

Know You More

Words and Music by Darlene Zschech

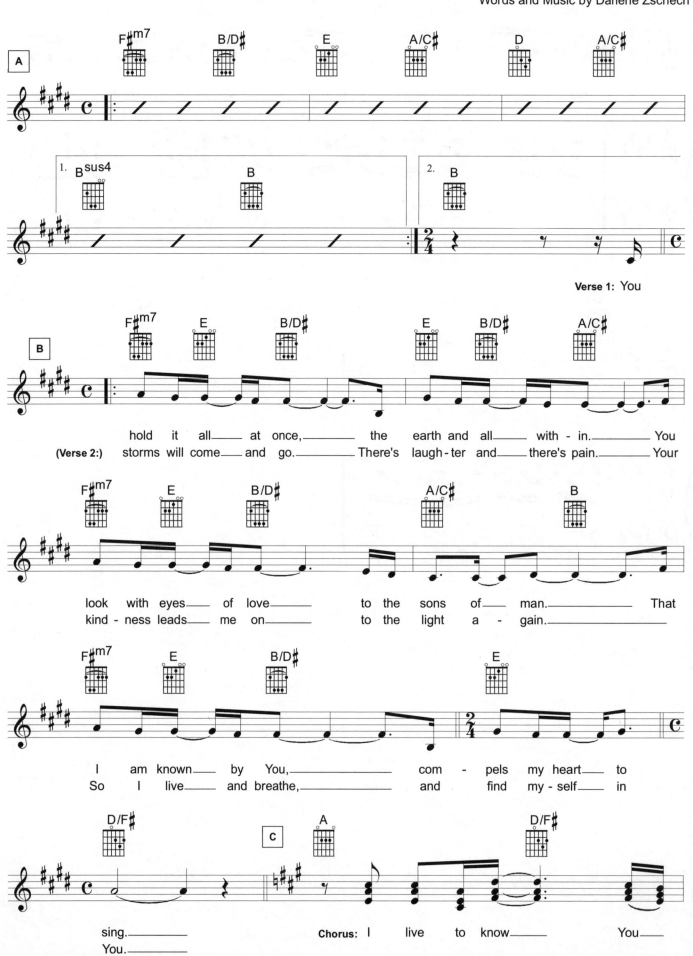

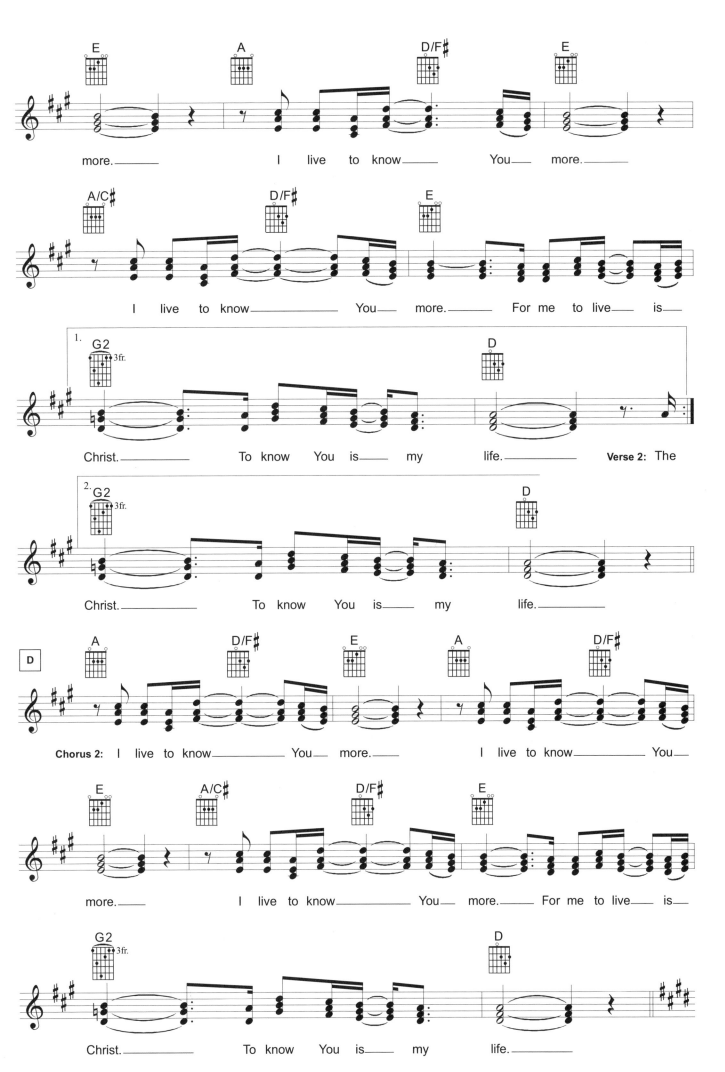

more._____ I live to know_____ You_____ more._____

I live to know_____ You_____ more._____ For me to live_____ is_____

1. Christ._____ To know You is____ my life._____ **Verse 2:** The

2. Christ._____ To know You is____ my life._____

Chorus 2: I live to know_____ You_____ more._____ I live to know_____ You_____

more._____ I live to know_____ You_____ more._____ For me to live_____ is_____

Christ._____ To know You is_____ my life._____

151

KNOW YOU MORE

Words and Music by Darlene Zschech

VERSE 1:
You hold it all at once
The earth and all within
You look with eyes of love
To the sons of man
That I am known by You
Compels my heart to sing

CHORUS:
I live to know You more
I live to know You more
I live to know You more
For me to live is Christ
To know You is my life

VERSE 2:
The storms will come and go
There's laughter and there's pain
Your kindness leads me on
To the light again
So I live and breathe
And find myself in You

© 2005 Darlene Zschech / Hillsong Publishing
PO Box 1195 Castle Hill NSW 1765 Australia
PH 61 2 8853 5353   FAX 61 2 9899 4591
E-Mail: publishing@hillsong.com

Hillsong
MUSIC AUSTRALIA

BRIDGE:

I live to know You
I live to know You
I live to know You more

VERSE 3:

I count it all but loss
Compared to knowing You
I give my life away
To know You any day

There Is Nothing Like

Words and Music by Jonas Myrin and Marty Sampson

there is no - thing like___ Your love.___ Your love.___

Last to

There is no - thing like,___ there is no - thing like___ Your love.___

Your love.___

Instrumental:

159

Bridge:

love You____ for-e-ver.____ I love You____ for-e-ver.____ I love You____ for-e-ver,____ Lord.____

I love You____ for-e-ver.____ I love You____ for-e-ver.____ I

160

love You ___ for - e - ver, ___ Lord. ___   I   love You ___ for - ever. ___ I

love You ___ for - e - ver. ___ I   love You ___ for - e - ver. ___ I   love You ___ for - e - ver. ___ I

cue vox on rpt

Pre Chorus 2:   And all__

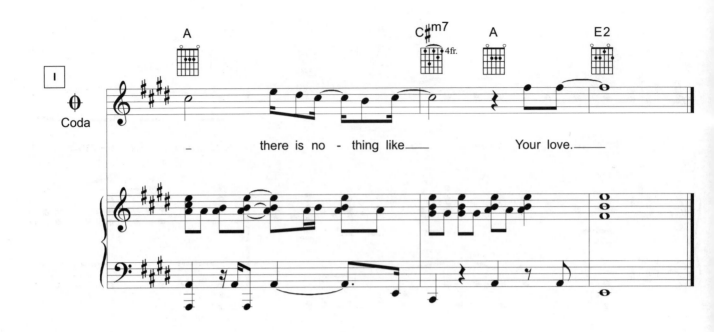

there is no - thing like____ Your love.____

There Is Nothing Like

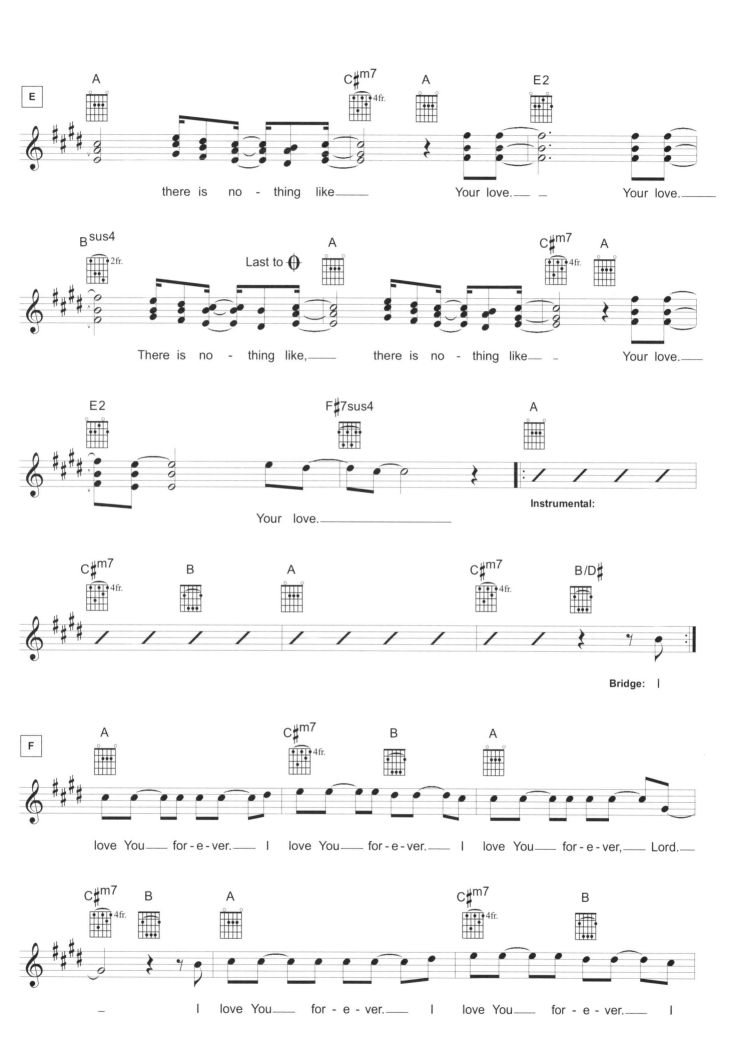

there is no - thing like____ Your love.__ - Your love.____

There is no - thing like,____ there is no - thing like____ - Your love.____

Your love._____

Instrumental:

Bridge: I

love You____ for - e - ver.____ I love You____ for - e - ver.____ I love You____ for - e - ver,____ Lord.____

- I love You____ for - e - ver.____ I love You____ for - e - ver.____ I

165

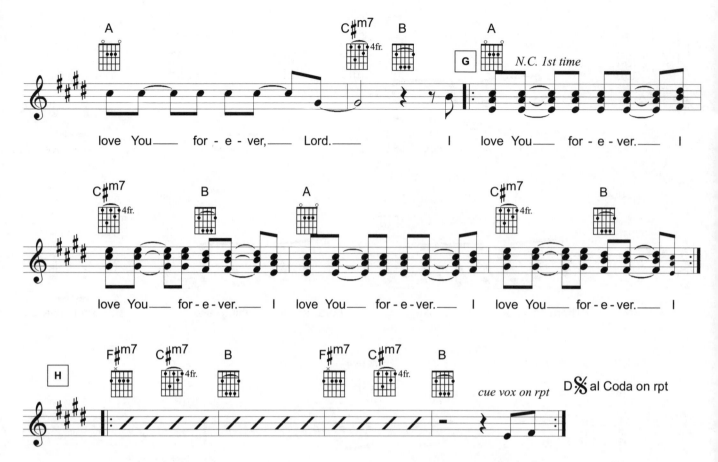

love You__ for - e - ver,__ Lord.__   I love You__ for - e - ver.__ I

love You__ for - e - ver.__ I love You__ for - e - ver.__ I love You__ for - e - ver.__ I

cue vox on rpt   D.S. al Coda on rpt

Pre Chorus 2: And all_

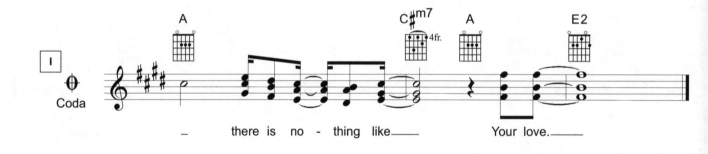

__   there is no - thing like__   Your love.

THERE IS NOTHING LIKE

Words and Music by Jonas Myrin and Marty Sampson

VERSE 1:
Father true and merciful
Bound to me with love
Adopted in
Free from all sin

VERSE 2:
Jesus Saviour glorified
Your offering none could give
I stand before You
Humbled and in awe

PRE CHORUS:
And all to You God
For all You are to me

CHORUS:
There is nothing like
There is nothing like
Your love
Your love

© 2004 Jonas Myrin and Marty Sampson / Hillsong
Publishing
PO Box 1195 Castle Hill NSW 1765 Australia
PH 61 2 8853 5353   FAX 61 2 9899 4591
E-Mail: publishing@hillsong.com

VERSE 3:
Holy Spirit
Gift of God
Teach my soul to soar
Train me in Your holy ways Lord

BRIDGE:
I love You forever
I love You forever
I love You forever Lord

What The World Will Never Take

Words and Music by Matt Crocker, Scott Ligertwood and Marty Sampson

Verse: With all I'm hol‑ding in‑side,___ with all my hopes and de‑si‑res.

And all the dreams that I've dreamt.___ With all I'm ho‑ping to be,___

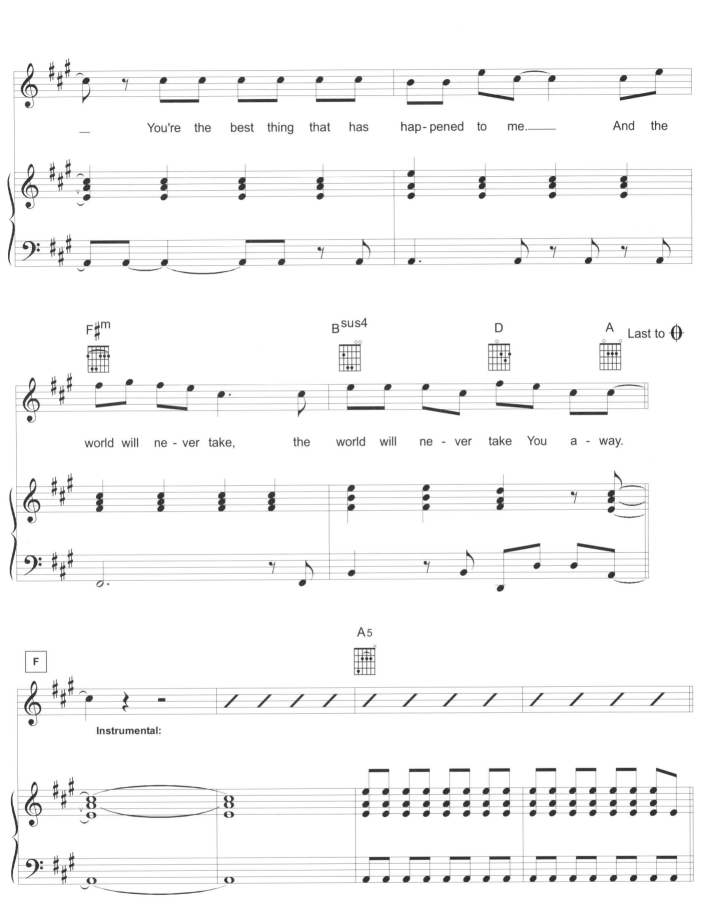

No one_____ could e - ver take You a - way._____ No one_____

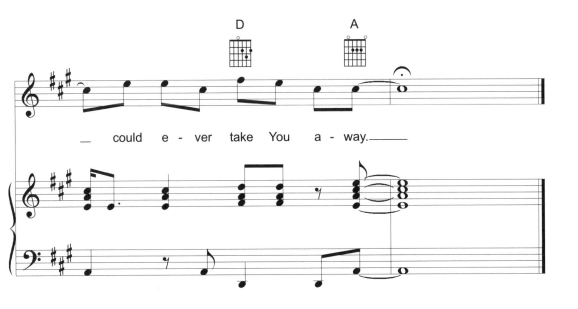

could e - ver take You a - way.

What The World Will Never Take

Words and Music by Matt Crocker, Scott Ligertwood and Marty Sampson

♩ = 125

Verse: With all I'm hol-ding in-side,____ with all my hopes and de-si-res.

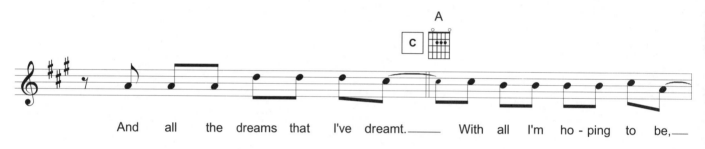

And all the dreams that I've dreamt.____ With all I'm ho-ping to be,____

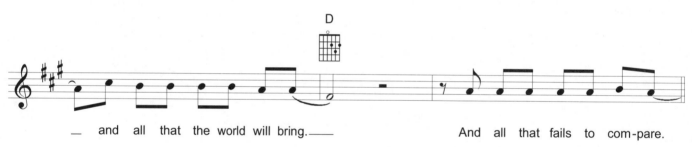

____ and all that the world will bring.____ And all that fails to com-pare.

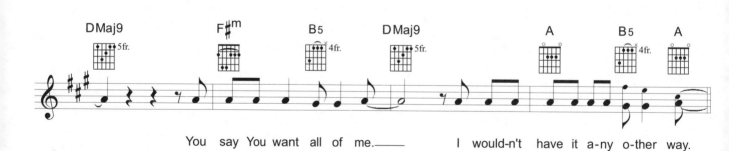

You say You want all of me.____ I would-n't have it a-ny o-ther way.

Chorus: I've got a Sa-viour, and He's li-ving in me.____ Whoa,____

I wan - na know, I wan - na know You to - day.

You're the best thing that has hap - pened to me. And the

world will ne - ver take, the world will ne - ver take You a - way.

Chorus 2: I've got a Sa - viour, and He's li - ving in me. Whoa,

I wan - na know, I wan - na know You to - day.

You're the best thing that has hap - pened to me. And the

world will ne - ver take, the world will ne - ver take You a - way.

Instrumental:

No one___ could e - ver take You a - way.___ No one___

___ could e - ver take You a - way.___

WHAT THE WORLD WILL NEVER TAKE

Words and Music by Matt Crocker, Scott Ligertwood and Marty Sampson

VERSE 1:
With all I'm holding inside
With all my hopes and desires
And all the dreams that I've dreamt
With all I'm hoping to be
And all that the world will bring
And all that fails to compare

PRE CHORUS:
You say You want all of me
I wouldn't have it any other way

© 2004 Matt Crocker, Scott Ligertwood and
Marty Sampson / Hillsong Publishing
PO Box 1195 Castle Hill NSW 1765 Australia
PH 61 2 8853 5353   FAX 61 2 9899 4591
E-Mail: publishing@hillsong.com

CHORUS:
**I've got a Saviour
And He's living in me
Whoa I wanna know
I wanna know You today
You're the best thing
That has happened to me
And the world will never take
The world will never take You away**

**No one could ever take You away
No one could ever take You away**

Tell The World

Words and Music by Jonathon Douglass, Joel Houston and Marty Sampson

Verse 1: Don't wan-na stand here and shout Your praise, and walk a-way and for-get Your Name.

Verse 2: No lon-ger I, but Christ in me. 'Cause it's the truth that set me free.

I stand for You if that's all I do,

How could this world be a bet-ter place,

'cause there is none that com-pares to You.__ **Pre Chorus:** 'Cause all I want__ in this
but by Thy mer-cy,_____ by Thy__ grace.

life time__ is You. And all I want__ in this

whole world__ is You, You.__ You.__

the world —— a-bout You. —————————— Come on, —— come on, —— we'll tell—

the world a - bout You. ———————— Come on,

You.

186

Tell The World

Words and Music by Jonathon Douglass, Joel Houston and Marty Sampson

Chorus: Tell the world that Je-sus lives. Tell the world that.

Tell the world that. Tell the world that He died for them.

Last to

1. Tell the world that He lives a-gain.

2, 4 Tell the world that He lives a-gain.

3. Tell the world that He lives a-gain.

E Drums

F Drums only 1st time

Bridge: Come on, come on, we'll tell

the world a-bout You. Come on,

come on, we'll tell the world a-bout You. Come on,

188

TELL THE WORLD
Words and Music by Jonathon Douglass, Joel Houston and Marty Sampson

VERSE 1:

Don't wanna stand here and shout
Your praise
And walk away and forget Your Name
I stand for You if that's all I do
'Cause there is none that compares to You

PRE CHORUS:

'Cause all I want in this lifetime is You
And all I want in this whole world is You

CHORUS:

Tell the world that Jesus lives
Tell the world that
Tell the world that
Tell the world that He died for them
Tell the world that He lives again

Hillsong
MUSIC AUSTRALIA

© 2004 Jonathon Douglass, Joel Houston and
Marty Sampson / Hillsong Publishing
PO Box 1195 Castle Hill NSW 1765 Australia
PH 61 2 8853 5353   FAX 61 2 9899 4591
E-Mail: publishing@hillsong.com

VERSE 2:
No longer I but Christ in me
'Cause it's the truth that set me free
How could this world be a better place
But by Thy mercy
By Thy grace

BRIDGE:
C'mon c'mon
We'll tell the world about You
C'mon c'mon
We'll tell the world about You